To Peter H. Lawrence
Vicar of Christ Church, Burney Lane, Ward End, Birmingham
and member of the East Birmingham Renewal Group

Words by Alison Fuggle

with other words by Roger Jones, Richard Owen,
Francis Pott, R.Heber and George Matheson

Christian Music Ministries
325 Bromford Road
Hodge Hill
Birmingham
B36 8ET

Tel: 021 783 3291
Fax: 021 785 0500

ISBN 1-874594-26-0
Cover design by Tracey Kesterton
Printed and bound by Charisma Design and Print Ltd.,
Lido House, Sansome Road, Shirley, Solihull, West Midlands.

CONTENTS

Narrator (during first 16 bars of opening song)
*The Revelation of Jesus Christ, which God gave to him, to show his servants things
which must shortly come to pass: and he sent and signified it by his angel to his
servant John:*
*Blessed is he that reads and they that hear the words of this prophecy, and keep those
things that are written therein: for the time is at hand.* (Rev. 1 v 1 , 3)

(1) ANGEL VOICES

Words by
Francis Pott

Music by
Roger Jones

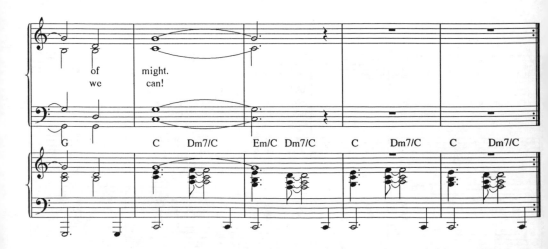

4

(A1)
(3) Yes, we know that Thou re- joi- cest
(4) In Thy house, great God, we of- fer
(TB)

C   Dm/C   Dm/C   Em/C   Em/C   Dm/C   B♭/C   F/C

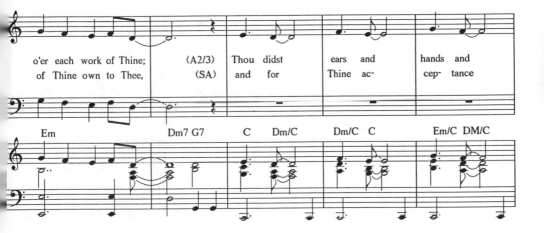

o'er each work of Thine; (A2/3) Thou didst ears and hands and
of Thine own to Thee, (SA) and for Thine ac- cep- tance

Em   Dm7 G7   C   Dm/C   Dm/C C   Em/C DM/C

voi- ces for thy praise de- sign; Crafts- man's art and
prof- fer, all un- wor- thi- ly, (all) hearts and minds and

B♭/C F/C   Em   Gsus4/D   G   B♭   Dm7/Bb   F/C   C

mu- sic's mea- sure for Thy plea- sure all
hands and voi- ces for in our choi- cest Psal-

Fm/Bb Bb   Ab/Eb Eb   F/G G   Ab   Gsus4

com- bi- dy. - - - Psal- - -ne.
mo- dy. - - - - - mo-

G   C Dm7/C   Em/C Dm7/C   C Dm7/C   C Dm7/C

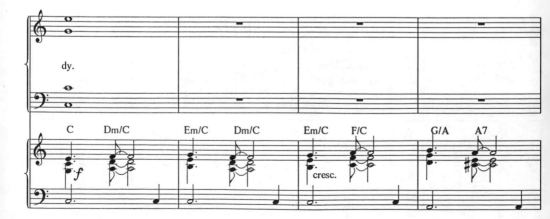

dy.

C Dm/C   Em/C Dm/C   Em/C F/C   G/A A7

cresc.

6

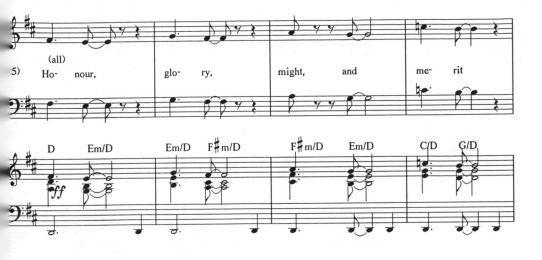

5)

(all)
Ho-nour, glo-ry, might, and me-rit

D   Em/D   Em/D F#m/D   F#m/D Em/D   C/D G/D
ff

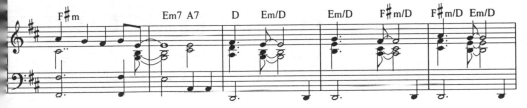

Thine shall e- ver be,   Fa- ther,   Son, and   Ho- ly

F#m   Em7 A7   D   Em/D   Em/D F#m/D   F#m/D Em/D

Spi- rit,   Bles- sed Tri- ni- ty.   Of the   best that

C/D   G/D   F#m   Asus4/D   A   C   Em7/C   G/D D

Thou hast gi- ven earth and hea- ven ren- der

Gm/C C B♭/F F G/A A B♭ Asus4 A

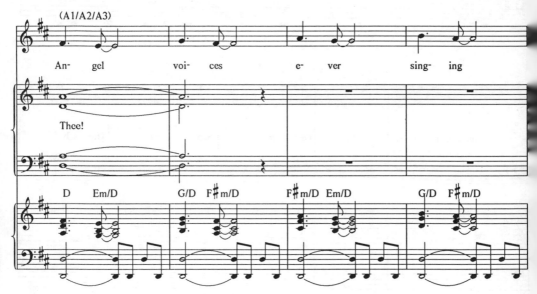

(A1/A2/A3)

An- gel voi- ces e- ver sing- ing

Thee!

D Em/D G/D F♯m/D F♯m/D Em/D G/D F♯m/D

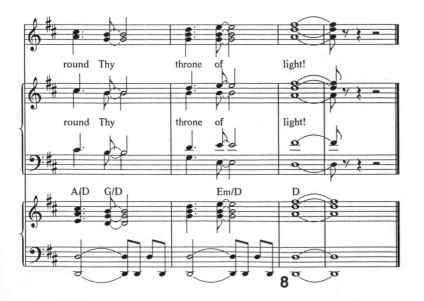

round Thy throne of light!

round Thy throne of light!

A/D G/D Em/D D

In exile on the remote island of Patmos for the crime of preaching the Good News about Jesus Christ, John receives a new call to give God's message to his people, and is granted a vision of power and glory, Jesus, the First and the Last.
[Rev.1.v 9 - 16]

Words by
Alison Fuggle

(2) I AM THE ONE

Music by
Roger Jones

To the clo- sing of the a- ges, com-ple-tion of my plan,

Dmaj7   Em11   D   F G A

3rd time to CODA

I AM, I am the One. And And

You are the One.

Dmaj7   Em11   Dmaj7   Em11

you, my be- lo- ved, I de- light in you.
you, my be- lo- ved, I de- light in you.

C   G   Em7   D   Em7   D

Long be- fore you ev- er knew me, I have cho- sen you,
Long be- fore all things ex- is- ted, I have cho- sen you.

C   G   Em7   D

10

formed you in the se- cret place, gen- tly brought you
You're so prec- ious in my eyes, you're a child of

in- to life, in- fi- nite- ly dear to me, my
God Most High. I have called you, I have loved you

trea- sure be- yond price!
for all time. You are mine!

I shall be there in the fu- ture as I was there

You are the One!

Em11 Bm F#m Em7

in the past. I am Al- pha and O-me- ga, I am the First,

F#m Gmaj7 F#m Em7

I am the Last! So for-e- ver

You are the First, and You are the Last!

A7 Dmaj7

and for-e- ver, 'til time shall be no more, I AM,

I am the One. I AM,

You are, You are the One.

(improvise/repeat to fade/end)

I am the One.

You are, You are the One.

This Jesus, risen, ascended and glorified, is the one whom all the hosts of heaven adore as they worship around his throne.
[Rev. 4 v 1 - 6]

(3) HOLY, HOLY, HOLY

Andante con moto ♩ = 90

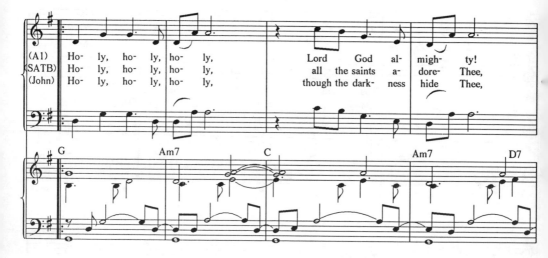

(A1) Ho- ly, ho- ly, ho- ly, Lord God al- migh- ty!
(SATB) Ho- ly, ho- ly, ho- ly, all the saints a- dore- Thee,
(John) Ho- ly, ho- ly, ho- ly, though the dark- ness hide Thee,

Ear- ly in the mor- ning our song shall rise to
cas- ting down their gol- den crowns a- round the glas- sy
though the eye of sin- ful man thy glo- ry may not

15

What a contrast between this and the broken, sinful world in which we, like John, live! Yet even in the glorious presence of the throne in heaven, rebellion once broke out. Lucifer, the son of the morning, otherwise known as the devil or Satan, thought to raise his head in pride against the Lord. His punishment was swift.
[Rev.12 v 7 - 9]

(4) WITH A CRASH OF THUNDER

(Choir divided into two equal parts)

With a crash of thun- der,

cast at last from hea- ven,

light- ning from the sky,

Lu- ci- fer   is   thrown to earth,

fal- ling from on   high,

19

Out you go!

Satan out you go! Out you go!

pui tranquillo - con moto

(Jesus) Beau- ty's turned to

Fmaj7   F7   Fmaj7   F7   Fmaj7

mp

a- shes, white robe's turned to dust,

F7   E7

pu- ri- ty by greed de-filed, love ex- changed for lust.

Fmaj7   F7   Fdim7

Thrown out of heaven, Satan turned his attention to the earth, the beautiful planet the Lord made as a home for men and women, lovingly formed in God's own image, the very pinnacle of his creation.

[Gen.3 v 1 - 6]

Just as he tempted Eve in the garden of Eden , so Satan continues his work of destruction throughout the ages. Just listen to the kind of things he says - how subtly he twists his words to try to deceive and corrupt.

**Words by
Alison Fuggle**

(5) WILL YOU BUY?

**Music by
Roger Jones**

back?

Ev'- ry love- ly thing,

back!

Ev'- ry love- ly thing,

Cm   Gm7   Cm   Gm7

pre- cious glit- ter- ing,

pre- cious glit- ter- ing,

here is ev'- ry thing

Cm   Gm7   Cm

(A1/A3)

you think you lack?

Ah-

you think you lack!

(A2)

So come, stake your claim for

Gm7   Cm   Fm/Ab

25

rich-es and fame, what- ev- er you name! There's no need to wait, it's

Fm   G7   A♭

here on a plate. Be- fore it's too late, will you buy!

A♭7   G7

Will you buy? Will you buy?   Will you buy? Will you buy?

Cm   Gm7   Cm   A♭maj7 Gm7

take the plunge to- day. Tru- ly, it's the way

take the plunge for tru- ly, it's the way

A♭maj7   Cm/G   Fm

to change your life.

to change your life.

Fm6/D   Dm7   G

2nd verse

(A1) No, don't hes- i- tate! Don't leave it too late!

(A2/A3/SATB) No, don't hes- i- tate!

Cm   Cm7   A♭maj7

mp

with pow'r and wealth.

with pow'r and wealth!

Fm6/D   Dm7/G   G

meno mosso - mysterioso

(A2) Don't you re-a-lise   you're not world-ly wise   if you mor-a-lise

A♭maj7   Fm9   Dm11

p

and stand and frown?   No need to be dense   or sit on the fence,

B♭dim7   Adim   G   A♭maj7   Fm9

com-pro-mise makes sense.   So come on   down!

D♭11   E♭maj9   F7   G

30

3rd time - CODA

(whisper!) Will you buy?

(whisper!) Will you buy?

Cm

After choosing to listen to Satan's lies instead of God's message of love, how could we hope to draw near the throne once more? By our own efforts never, for God cannot tolerate sin. But there is a way, one which even the angels can barely understand: when we could no longer draw near to him, God himself reached down to us .
[Rev 5 v 1 - 10]

Words by
Richard Owen and Roger Jones

(6) BEHOLD THE LAMB!

Music by
Roger Jones

Moderato piangevole ♩ = 95

(A2)

Be-hold, the Lamb!

(Capo on 1)
D   Em7   D   D   Em7   D   Em7   D   Em7

mp

(1st A2/2nd SA)

(1st John/2nd TB)   Be- hold the Lamb   of God!   Be- hold the Lamb!

Be- hold the Lamb!   The   Lamb of God!

D   Em7   D   Em7

mf

31

Only Jesus , completely human and yet free from sin, could pay the price for the sins of the world . He alone is worthy to receive power, and wealth, and wisdom and strength and honour, and glory and praise.
[Rev. 5 v 11 - 14]
We join with the angels and everything in earth and heaven as we declare his glory.

(7) WORTHY IS THE LAMB

Words and Music
by Roger Jones

po- wer, wealth and wis- dom, strength and ho- nour,

Dm   B♭   C   Csus4 C

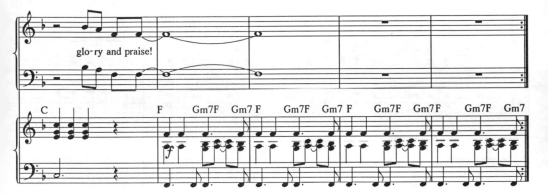

glo- ry and praise!

C   F   Gm7F Gm7 F Gm7F Gm7 F Gm7F Gm7F Gm7F Gm7

Lord, you are wor- thy, to re- ceive glo- ry,

E♭   F   E♭   F

glo- ry and ho- nour and power,

A♭   G♭   Csus4   C

For you cre- a- ted, all things cre- a- ted.

E♭   F   E♭   F

They have their be- ing in you!

A♭   G♭   Csus4   C

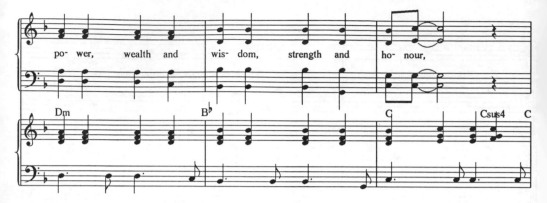

po- wer, wealth and wis- dom, strength and ho- nour,

Dm   B♭   C   Csus4   C

Last time to Coda

glo- ry and praise!

C   F   Gm7 F   Gm7 F   Gm7 F   Gm7 F   Gm7 F   Gm7

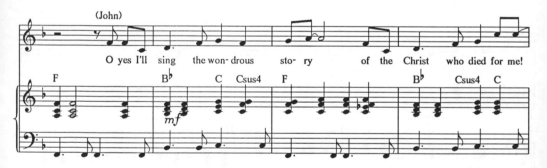

(John)

O yes I'll sing the won- drous sto- ry of the Christ who died for me!

F   B♭   C   Csus4   F   B♭   Csus4   C

mf

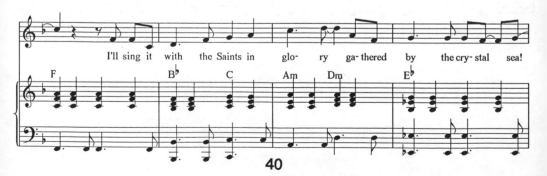

I'll sing it with the Saints in glo- ry ga- thered by the cry- stal sea!

F   B♭   C   Am   Dm   E♭

The Lamb enthroned in heaven is still the same Jesus who promised that he would be with his disciples to the very end of time. To John he renews this promise and gives a new commission, to tell others of that love which will never change.

Words by
George Matheson

(8) O LOVE THAT WILL NOT LET ME GO

Music by
Roger Jones

(John)

O love that will not let me go, I
rest my wea-ry soul in Thee; I give Thee
back the life I owe, that in Thine o-cean
depths its flow may ri-cher, ful-ler be.

O

43

Light that fol- lows all my way, I

(SA) that fol- lows all my way,

C   Em/B   Am   C/G

mp

yield my flick'- ring torch to Thee; My

my flick'- ring torch to Thee;

F   C   Dm7   Gsus4 G7

heart re- stores its bor- rowed ray, that

re- stores its bor- rowed ray,

Esus4   E7   Am   C/G

in Thy sun- shine's blaze its day may brigh- ter, fai- rer

in Thy sun- shine's blaze its day brigh- ter, fai- rer

F   G/F   C   Dm7   Gsus4   G7

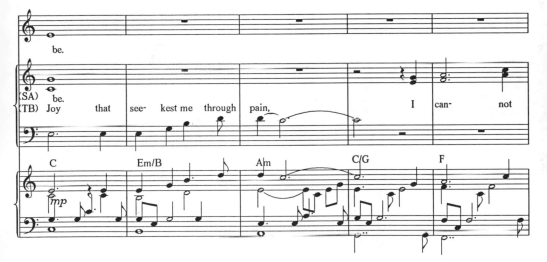

be.

(SA) be.
(TB) Joy that see- kest me through pain, I can- not

C   Em/B   Am   C/G   F

mp

close my heart to Thee; I trace the

cresc.

C   Dm7   Gsus4   G7   Esus4

cresc.

8

45

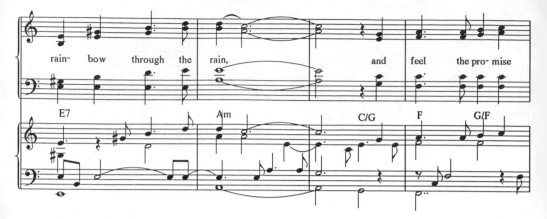

rain- bow through the rain, and feel the pro- mise

is not vain that morn shall tear- less

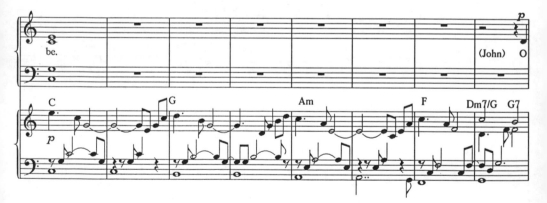

be. (John) O

cross that lif- test up my head, I

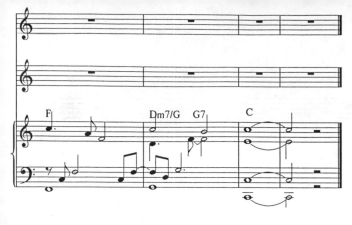

Though Jesus is seated on the throne of heaven, he is not remote from us. He still
reaches out with words of love, calling us back to him and longing for us to respond .
[Rev. 1 v 19 - 3 v 18 - Letters to the churches]

Words by
Alison Fuggle

(9) LISTEN TO ME

Music by
Roger Jones

learn now, give ear,   All who love

G   F

me now hear.   Hear what I say!

Dm7   G   Am

cresc.   f

O hear what I say,   To the chur- ches to- day:

F   Dm7   Gsus4

lis- ten to me!

G   C

p

(A1)

(1) Your love's grown cold,   Dus- ty and
(2) Love is the name,   free- dom the

B♭   C   B♭

mp

49

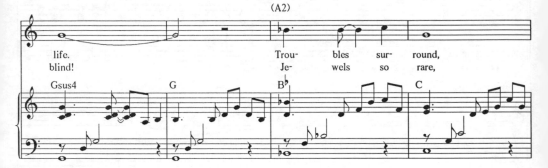

50

(A1) (A2)

If you've be- lieved, ful- ly re-
Turn from your sin, lis- ten to

C F C

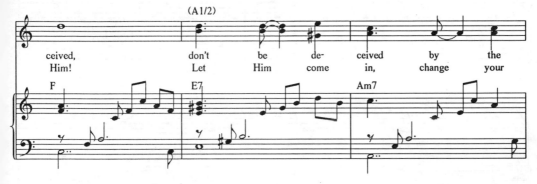

(A1/2)

ceived, don't be de- ceived by the
Him! Let Him come in, change your

F E7 Am7

lies!
mind!

F Dm7 Gsus4 G7 Gsus4 G7

1st time

(Jesus) Lis- ten to me! Lis- ten to me!

C

mp

51

Lis- ten to me! Lis- ten to me!

2nd time

(Jesus) Lis- ten to me! Lis- ten to me!

Lis- ten to me! Lis- ten to me!

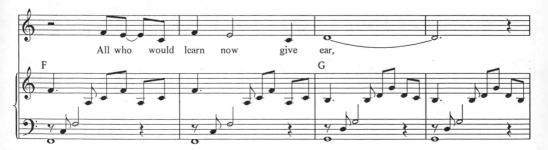

All who would learn now give ear,

All who love me now hear.

Hear what I say! O hear what I say,

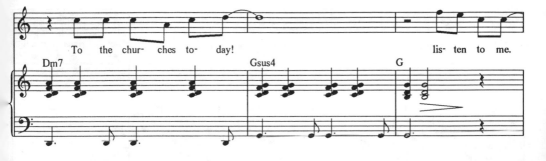

To the chur- ches to- day! lis- ten to me.

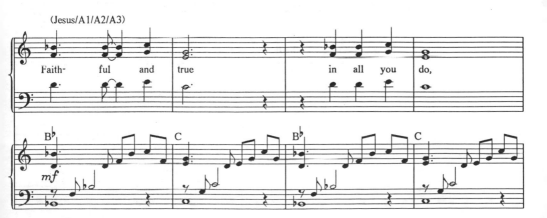

(Jesus/A1/A2/A3)

Faith- ful and true in all you do,

53

Trials you en- dure for His name.

Fm   B♭   E♭   Fm Gsus4   G

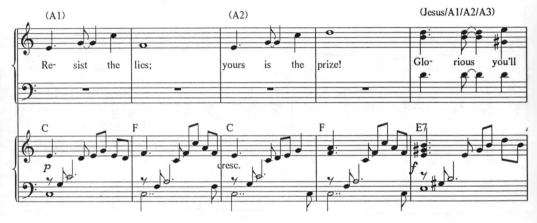

(A1)   (A2)   (Jesus/A1/A2/A3)

Re- sist the lies; yours is the prize! Glo- rious you'll

C   F   C   F   E7

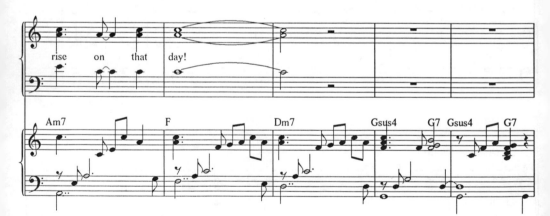

rise on that day!

Am7   F   Dm7   Gsus4   G7 Gsus4   G7

(Jesus)

Lis- ten to me! Lis- ten to me!

C

Lis- ten to me! Lis- ten to me!

p

rall.

No narration here; next song follows immediately.

Words by
Alison Fuggle

(10) HERE I STAND

Music by
Roger Jones

capo on 1   *Andante*   ♩ = 70

(Jesus)

Here I stand,   here I stand   at the door   and knock.

If on- ly you   will hear my   voice and let me in!

C   F   G   C   Am7

If you will just re- lease   the lock!   Here I stand,

F   Dm7   Dm7/G G   C

here I stand   wait- ing just   out- side.

Dm7   F   G   C

If on- ly you   will hear my   voice and let me in!   If you will let me come   in- side!

F   G   C   Am7   F   Dm7

Lis- ten to the words   I   long to say   to you,   to

Dm7/G   G   F   G   C   G   Am7

tell you once a- gain   how much I   love.   Lis- ten to   the long- ing of my

F   G   C   Dm7 C   F   G

heart   to   have   you   near,   O   lis- ten to   my   words   of

C   G   Am7   F   Dm7

last time to Coda

love.   O   lis- ten to   my   words   of   love!

Gsus4   G   Dm7   Gsus4   G   C

Instruments Only

Dm7   F   G   C   F   G

C   Am7   F   Dm7   Dm7/G   G   C

Dm7   F   G   C

57

The call to John, and to all of us, is not a call to struggle against impossible odds, but a call to share in victory. By the blood of the Lamb, each child of God has the power and authority to overcome, and to say with the Angels, "Satan, out you go!"
[Rev. 20 v 1 - 10]

Words by
Alison Fuggle

(11) RULE OF NIGHT IS OVER!

Music by
Roger Jones

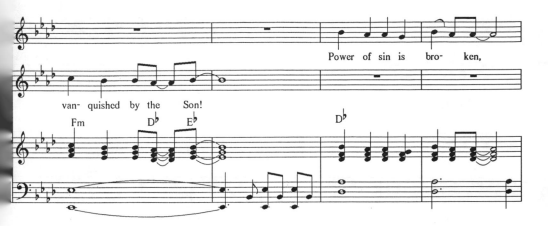

Power of sin is bro- ken,
van- quished by the Son!

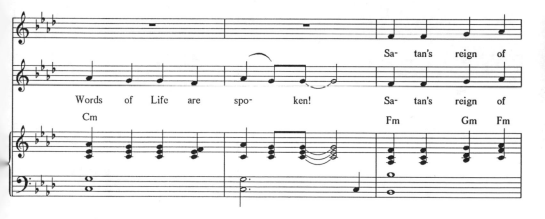

Words of Life are spo- ken! Sa- tan's reign of
Sa- tan's reign of

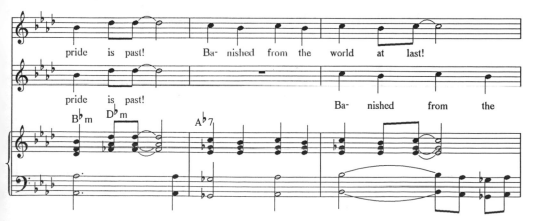

pride is past! Ba- nished from the world at last!
pride is past! Ba- nished from the

Ba- nished from the world at last!

world at last! From the world at last!

Sa- tan van- quished from the world! Down in- to the pit is

Out you go!

Fm E♭ Fm E♭ D♭ E♭

ff

hurled! Night is ba- nished from the earth! All cre- a- tion knows new

Out you go! Out you go!

Fm E♭ Fm E♭ D♭ E♭

60

worth! All cre-a- tion knows new worth!

Night is ba- nished from the earth!

Now the rain- bow marks it's birth!

Now the rain- bow marks it's birth! Sa- tan out you go!

Sa- tan out you go! Out you go!

Sa- tan out you go! Out you go!

From the earth for- e- ver the e- vil one is thrown!

Powers and do-mi-na- tions be- fore the Lamb have flown!

Christ is lif- ted o- ver all!

At His feet all na- tions fall!

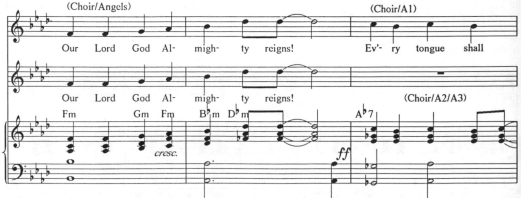

(Choir/Angels)

Our Lord God Al- migh- ty reigns! Ev'- ry tongue shall

Our Lord God Al- migh- ty reigns!

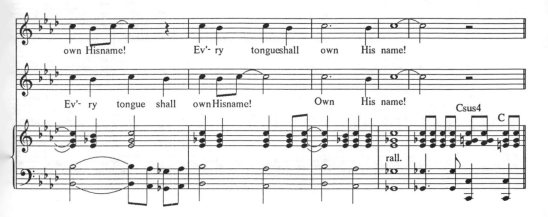

own His name! Ev'- ry tongue shall own His name!

Ev'- ry tongue shall own His name! Own His name!

Csus4 C

rall.

Allegro ma non troppo ♩ = 130

(SATB) Wor- thy is the Lamb, wor- thy is the Lamb who was slain,

F   B♭9   F   A♭   B♭/C

Wor- thy is the Lamb, wor- thy is the Lamb who was slain,

F   B♭9   F   F♭/F

To re-ceive po-wer, wealth and wis-dom, strength and ho-nour,

B♭ C Dm B♭ G Csus4

glo-ry and praise!

Last time to Coda

C F Gm7 F Gm7 F Gm7 F Gm7 F Gm7 F Gm7 F Gm7 F Gm7 F Gm7

Lord, you are wor-thy, to re-ceive glo-ry,

E♭ F E♭ F

mf

glo- ry and ho- nour and power,

A♭   G♭   Csus4   C

For you cre- a- ted, all things cre- a- ted.

E♭   F   E♭   F

They have their be- ing in you!

D.S.

A♭   G♭   Csus4   C

CODA

(Angels harmonise)

Wor- thy is the Lamb!

Although Satan will be defeated in the end, each individual must still choose which way to follow. All will be accountable to God when, at the end of time, a final judgment is made.

[Rev. 20 v 11 - 15]

Words by
Alison Fuggle

(12) ARE YOU IN THE BOOK?

Music by
Roger Jones

moderato   ♩. = 70   (A3)

At

last the time has come, the end- ing of the age, com-

ple- tion of the plan, cre-a- tion's fi- nal page. The

Fmaj7 Dm7   G7   Cmaj7   G7

wri- ting's on the wall, the ul- ti- mate roll- call, so

Dm7   G7   Em   Am7

now we ask you all - Are you in the Book? On

Fmaj7   G9   Cmaj7 Fmaj7 Cmaj7 Fmaj7

ev'- ry sheet, in let- ters neat, lis- ted com- plete those who be- lieve.
not too late to change your fate. Why did you wait so long to choose?

D   E   D   E   Am   Am7

Here's ev'-ry- one, and what they've done,
The Day will come when all is done,

D9   Dm7

each child the Son waits to re- ceive.
too late to run and all to lose! the

Em7   Am   Am7

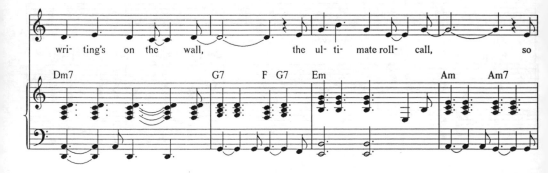

wri- ting's on the wall, the ul- ti- mate roll- call, so

Dm7   G7   F G7 Em   Am   Am7

2nd time to Coda

now we ask you all: Are you in the Book? It's

Dm7 G   Dm7   C   F   C   F

CODA   (spoken)

So now we ask you all: Are you in the Book?

nb. *Some Chords differ in Accompaniment Cassette*

How happy are those whose name is written in the book of life! Jesus welcomes them to stand at his side in a world transformed and redeemed from Satan's rule.

Narrator (during instrumental passage before verse1)
Then I saw a new heaven and a new earth, for the first heaven and the first earth had passed away and the sea was no more . And I saw the holy city, new Jerusalem, coming down out of heaven from God, prepared as a bride adorned for her husband; and I heard a great voice from the throne saying, "Behold, the dwelling of God is with men; he will dwell with them, and they shall be his people, and God himself shall be with them and be their God."
(Rev 21 v 1 - 3)
Narrator (during instrumental passage before verse 2)
"Behold, the dwelling of God is with men; he will dwell with them, and they shall be his people , and God himself shall be with them and be their God. He shall wipe away every tear from their eyes; and there shall be no more death, nor sorrow, nor crying, neither shall there be any more pain: for the former things are passed away." And he who sat upon the throne said," Behold, I make all things new."
(Rev 21 v 3 -5)

Words by
Alison Fuggle

(13) NO MORE DYING

Music by
Roger Jones

(1st time - A2)
(2nd time - Jesus)

There'll be no more dy- ing, no more cry- ing there!
There'll be no more dy- ing, no more cry- ing there!

No more sor- row, no more sigh- ing,
Ce- le- bra- tion, ju- bi- la- tion

Em7 D C G

there'll be no more pain! Death it- self is
at my wed- ding feast! I the Bride- groom

Em7 D C

con- quered by his fi- nal vic- to- ry!
call to you! Come, my Bride and take your place!

Em7 D C Em7 D

All cre- a- tion now cre- a- ted once a- gain!
I have called you, I have loved you for all time!

F G F Gm F

Once a- gain!
You are mine!

G   Asus4   A7

(Jesus)

At cre- a- tion's fi- nal pa- ges, when time it- self

Dmaj7   Em11   D   F

shall cease, I AM, I am the One.

(A2/A3) You are,

G   A   Dmaj7   Em11   Dmaj7

At the clo- sing of the a- ges,

You are the One.

Em11   Dmaj7   Em11

sal- va-tion's plan com- plete, I AM, I am the One.

I shall be there in the fu- ture

You are the One.

as I was there in the past. I am Al- pha

and Omeg- a, I am the First, I am the Last!

You are the First, and

So for- e- ver and for- e- ver,

you are the Last!

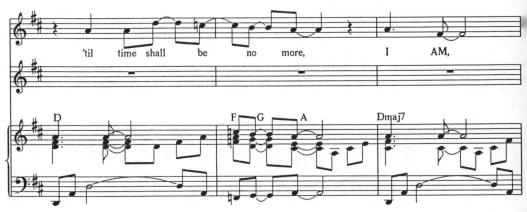

'til time shall be no more, I AM,

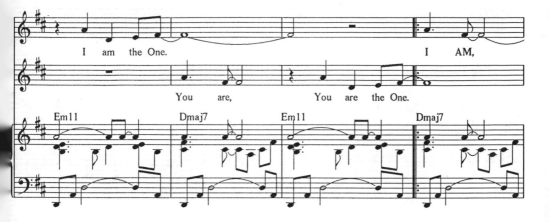

To all who hear and respond to his call, Jesus gives the right to enter the new Jerusalem, the city of God adorned with jewels and filled with his glory. Here at last we shall gaze upon the face of our Lord and worship him forever.
[Rev. 21 v 9 - 22 v 5,14]

(14) EVERLASTING JOY

head!

E- ver- last- ing joy!

head!

E- ver- last- ing joy - - !

E- ver- last- ing joy!

E- ver- last- ing joy

3rd time D.S.
4th time to CODA

E- ver- last- ing joy shall crown your head!

shall crown your head!

(1st time - John)
(2nd time - A3)

(1) The ci- ty of our God has come, the ho- ly new Je-
(2) The ran- somed of the Lord shall come with sing- ing to Je-

mf

77

ru-sa- lem,   for God with man has   made His dwel- ling place!
ru-sa- lem!   The ve- ry stones with   songs of joy re- sound!

ev'- ry   race,   His cho- sen ones who
e- ver   where   the streams of li- ving

And ga- thered there from
The thir- sty drink for-

hear His   call,   with   e- ver last- ing   joy shall see His   face!
wat- er   spring,   and   e- ver last- ing   joy shall be their   crown!

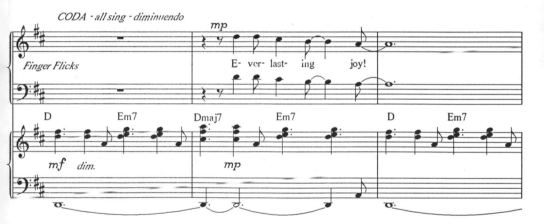

CODA - *all sing - diminuendo*

Finger Flicks

E- ver- last- ing   joy!

E- ver- last- ing   joy!

E- ver- last- ing   joy!

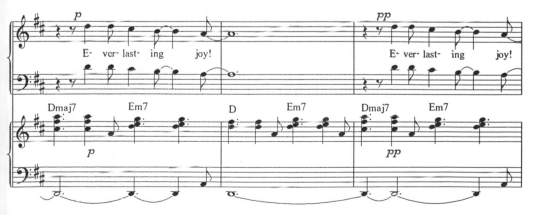

Everlasting joy!

Possible Descant(s) for Angels
in final Chorus - plus improvisations

(1) Praise the Lord, the King of Kings!

(2) Lord of

Songs of

Lords, the Prince of Peace!

joy be-gin and ne-ver cease!

Be-gin and ne-ver cease!

The Spirit and the Bride say, "Come." And let him who hears say," Come." And let
him who is thirsty come, let him who desires take the water of life without price.
He who testifies to these things says, "Surely I am coming soon."
Amen. Even so, come, Lord Jesus! (Rev. 22 vv 17, 20)

Words by
Roger Jones

(15) COMING WITH THE CLOUDS

Music by
Roger Jones

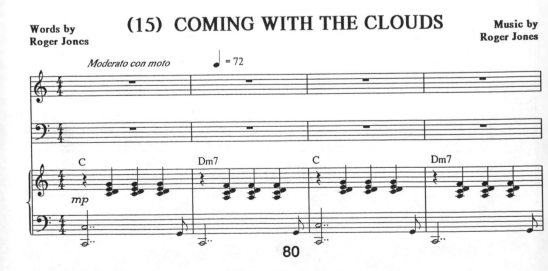

Moderato con moto ♩ = 72

CODA

suggested improvistions

(This section freely repeated)

(Response - here appropriate words may be said, e.g. Short Talk, Prayers, Silence, Words of Knowledge, etc., enabling everyone to respond to the message of the musical.)

Words by
Alison Fuggle

Music by
Roger Jones

(16) HERE I STAND (reprise)

capo on 1

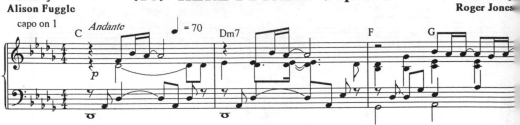

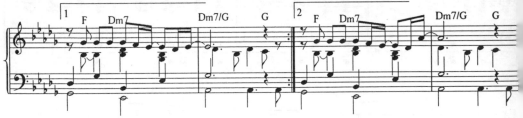

(Jesus)

Here I stand,   here I stand   at the door   and knock.

If on- ly you   will hear my   voice and let me in!

If you will just re- lease the lock! Here I stand,

here I stand wait- ing just out- side.

If on- ly you will hear my voice and let me in!

If you will let me come in- side! Lis- ten to the words I

No narration here; final song follows immediately.

(17) ANGEL VOICES (Reprise)

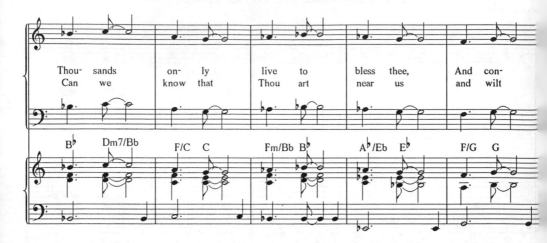

Thou- sands   on- ly   live   to   bless   thee,   And con-
Can   we   know   that   Thou   art   near   us   and   wilt

B♭   Dm7/Bb   F/C   C   Fm/Bb B♭   A♭/Eb E♭   F/G   G

1st time

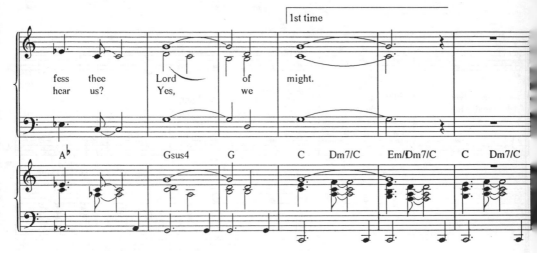

fess   thee,   Lord   of   might.
hear   us?   Yes,   we

A♭   Gsus4   G   C   Dm7/C   Em/Dm7/C   C   Dm7/C

2nd time

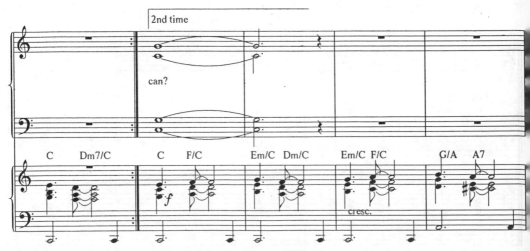

can?

C   Dm7/C   C   F/C   Em/C Dm/C   Em/C F/C   G/A   A7

f   cresc.

90

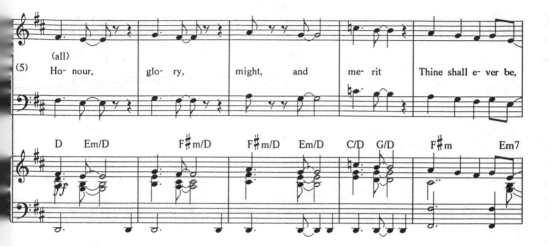

(5) (all)
Ho- nour, glo- ry, might, and me- rit Thine shall e- ver be,

D Em/D F♯m/D F♯m/D Em/D C/D G/D F♯m Em7

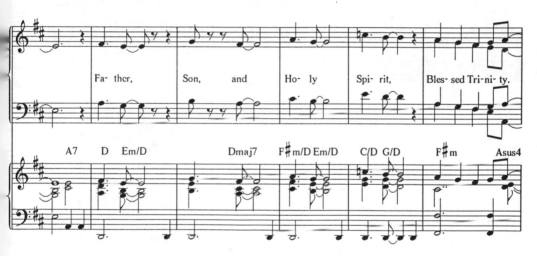

Fa- ther, Son, and Ho- ly Spi- rit, Bles- sed Tri- ni- ty.

A7 D Em/D Dmaj7 F♯m/D Em/D C/D G/D F♯m Asus4

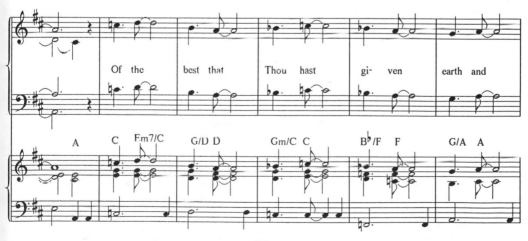

Of the best that Thou hast gi- ven earth and

A C Fm7/C G/D D Gm/C C B♭/F F G/A A